SATs prep of epic proportions from CGP!

This SAT Buster Book 2 is bursting with more Number, Ratio and Algebra questions — perfect prep for the KS2 Maths SATs Reasoning papers.

We've covered all the skills pupils will need, with friendly self-assessment tick boxes to help them keep track of their progress on each topic.

There's also a handy scoresheet at the back to record all their marks, so it's easy to see how they're getting on overall!

What CGP is all about

Our sole aim here at CGP is to produce the highest quality books — carefully written, immaculately presented and dangerously close to being funny.

Then we work our socks off to get them out to you — at the cheapest possible prices.

Published by CGP

Editors: Michael Bushell, Samuel Mann and Caroline Purvis

ISBN: 978 1 78908 137 4

With thanks to Ruth Greenhalgh for the proofreading.
Also thanks to Laura Jakubowski for the copyright research.

Printed by Bell & Bain Ltd, Glasgow.
Clipart from Corel®

Based on the classic CGP style created by Richard Parsons.

Contents

Here's what you have to do...

In Year 6 you have to take some tests called the SATs. This book will help you do well in the number, ratio & algebra questions on the maths tests.

This is a Number Adder — it can handle even the trickiest calculations.

Your aim is to become a Number Adder.

Work through the questions in the book. When you finish a topic, add up your marks and write them in the scoresheet at the end of the book.

Then, put a tick in the box at the end of the topic to show how you got on.

If you got a lot of questions wrong, put a tick in the circle on the left. Don't worry — every Number Adder has to start somewhere. Make sure you know your number, ratio and algebra rules inside out, then have another go.

If you're nearly there but your maths is still a bit wobbly, put a tick in the middle circle. Ask your teacher to help you work out the areas you need more practice on.

If you're really confident and got nearly all the questions right, tick the circle on the right.

Congratulations — you're a Number Adder!

Place Value and Roman Numerals

Answer these questions to see how much you know about place value and Roman numerals.

1) What is **2040** in words? Tick the box.

   Two hundred and forty ☐   **Twenty-four thousand** ☐

   Two thousand and forty ☐   **Two hundred and four** ☐

   1 mark

2) What is the value of each of these digits in **486 173**?
   Give your answers in **numbers**.

   1 ....   6 ....   4 ....

   2 marks

3) Write out the following in **numbers**.

   Five thousand, five hundred and sixty-two.   ....

   Seven hundred and seventeen thousand.   ....

   One million, nine hundred and eighty-seven.   ....

   2 marks

4) Annie can't remember her school ID number. She says:

   "I know it has a 3 in the hundred thousands place, and a 7 in the tens place."

   Which of the numbers below could be Annie's ID number? Circle your answer.

   1 234 567   4 321 987   1 357 975   3 531 975

   1 mark

5) Look at the Roman numerals below.
   Circle the largest number. Underline the even number.

   CLVII   MIII   DCCXXX   CCCV   LXIX

   2 marks

6) Write the following numbers in Roman numerals. One has been done for you.

   565   DLXV ⬅ 565 = 500 + 50 + 10 + 5   110   ....

   2009   1960   ....

   2 marks

A Number Adder knows the place value of
every digit in a number. Do you? Tick the box.

Ordering Numbers and Rounding

You'll need to know how to put numbers in order and when to round them up or down. Test your knowledge by trying out these questions.

1) Put these numbers in order. Start with the **smallest**.

| 326 | 578 | 145 | 191 | 399 | 600 |

| | | | | | |

smallest ⟶ largest

1 mark

2) Here are some signs:

Write the correct sign in each of these boxes.

20 + 5 [ ] 30 − 5   8 × 3 [ ] 7 × 4   45 ÷ 5 [ ] 14 ÷ 2

2 marks

3) Padma wants to count upwards in steps of **100**, starting at **5812**.

Fill in the gaps in Padma's sequence.

5812 [ ] [ ] 6112 [ ] [ ]

What is the first number in Padma's sequence that is more than 7000?

....

2 marks

4) Here is a number line. Write in the three missing numbers in the empty boxes.

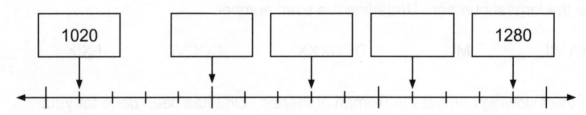

1 mark

5) Frank thinks of a whole number.

When he multiplies the number by **8**, the answer is **more than 70**.

When he multiplies the number by **4**, the answer is **less than 40**.

What is Frank's number? ....

1 mark

Ordering Numbers and Rounding

6) Circle the highest number in each box.

| 14 | 16 | 9 |

| −6 | 4 | 0 |

| −23 | −5 | −7 |

| −99 | −100 | −101 |

2 marks

7) Gus has £200 in his bank account in January.
Every month, £70 is subtracted from his account.
Complete the table.

In what month will Gus' bank account
go below −£250?

....

Month	Bank Account
Jan	£200
Feb	£130
Mar	
Apr	
May	
Jun	−£150

2 marks

8) Remy measures the temperature in his fridge and his freezer.
Mark these temperatures on the number line below:

The temperature in the fridge is **2 °C**. Label this **A**.

The temperature in the freezer is **−18 °C**. Label this **B**.

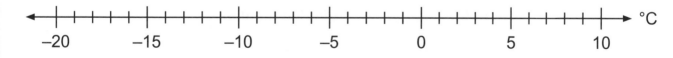

What is the difference in temperature between the fridge and the freezer?

...............................°C

Remy accidentally leaves the freezer open.
The temperature in the freezer goes up by **4 °C**.
What is the new temperature in the freezer?

...............................°C

3 marks

Section 1 — Number and Ratio

Ordering Numbers and Rounding

9) Look at the numbers below.

Circle the number that is closest to 150.

Underline the number that is furthest from 150.

| 75 | 220 | 101 | 1501 | 0 | _____ |

2 marks

10) Round these numbers to the nearest 10. One has been done for you.

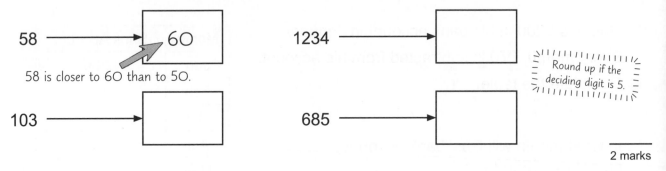

58 ⟶ 60

58 is closer to 60 than to 50.

1234 ⟶

Round up if the deciding digit is 5.

103 ⟶

685 ⟶

2 marks

11) Round these numbers to the nearest 1000. Write your answers in the boxes.

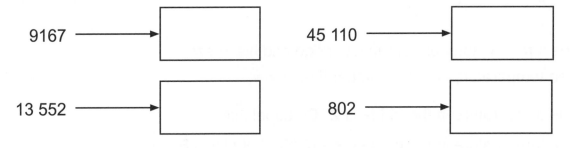

9167 ⟶

45 110 ⟶

13 552 ⟶

802 ⟶

2 marks

12) Complete the table to show how the number **7 384 912** can be rounded.

One has been done for you.

To the nearest...	Rounded number
10	7 384 910
100	
1000	
10 000	
100 000	

2 marks

Number Adders love wrapping their brains around rounded numbers. What about you? Tick the box.

Decimals

The digits that come after a decimal point show tenths, hundredths and thousandths.
Check how well you know decimals by trying out these questions.

1) What is the value of the **5** in the numbers below? Give your answers in **words**.

9.05 ....

0.501 ....

12.2052 ....

2 marks

2) Look at the number line below.

```
        A              B                C                          D
        ↓              ↓                ↓                          ↓
◄—+++++++++++|+++++++++++|+++++++++++|+++++++++++|+++++++++++|—►
  2           3           4           5           6
```

Write the value of each letter in the boxes. One has been done for you.

A [2.4]   **B** [   ]   **C** [   ]   **D** [   ]

A is 4 tenths greater than 2 on the number line.

2 marks

3) Write down the following as decimals.

four tenths ....   seven hundredths ....

four tenths **plus** seven hundredths ....

2 marks

Compare each digit in turn, starting with the digit with the largest place value.

4) Jane is measuring the mass of some of the objects on her desk.
Put these masses in order. Start with the **heaviest**.

| 0.98 kg | 1.9 kg | 1.101 kg | 0.345 kg | 1.29 kg |

.... kg   .... kg   .... kg   .... kg   .... kg

heaviest ——————————————————————————————► lightest

1 mark

Section 1 — Number and Ratio

Decimals

5) Here is a number line. Write the missing numbers in the empty boxes.

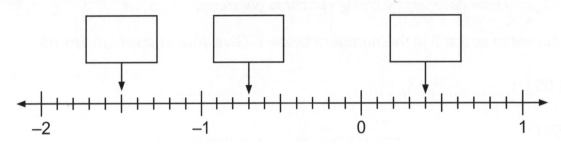

_____
2 marks

6) What is **one point six** minus **three point eight**?

Use the number line to help. ....

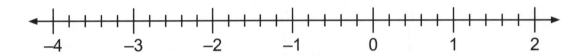

_____
1 mark

7) Round each of these decimals to the nearest tenth. One has been done for you.

0.762 | 0.8 | 4.813 [   ]   53.09 [   ]   0.949 [   ]

0.762 is closer to 0.8 than to 0.7.

_____
2 marks

8) The distance between Derek's house and the park is **0.432 km**.

Round this distance to the nearest hundredth. ...._km_

Eleni's house is **12.892 km** away from Derek's house.

Round this distance to 1 decimal place. ...._km_ _____
2 marks

9) Circle all of the numbers below that round to **10**
when rounded to the nearest whole number.

    9.92   11.01   1.023   9.495   10.388   9.724

_____
2 marks

Number Adders get the point of decimals. Do you?
Tick the box to show how you feel about these questions.

Fractions

These questions cover all sorts of fraction skills. Have a go and see how much you know.

1) Match each shape to the fraction that shows what proportion of the shape is shaded.

The fractions are written in their simplest forms.

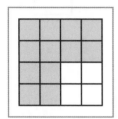 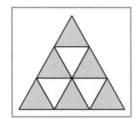 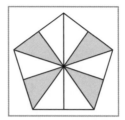 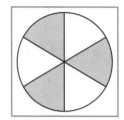

$\dfrac{1}{2}$ $\dfrac{2}{3}$ $\dfrac{3}{4}$ $\dfrac{2}{5}$

2 marks

2) Write these fractions in their simplest form.

$\dfrac{26}{30}$ ⬚ $\dfrac{9}{33}$ ⬚ $\dfrac{18}{63}$ ⬚

2 marks

3) Jessica has made a cake. She wants to take $\dfrac{2}{3}$ of the cake to school.

She cuts the cake into 24 equal slices.

How many slices should she take to school?

.... *slices*

1 mark

4) Look at the fractions below.

Circle the fraction that is equivalent to $\dfrac{1}{4}$.

Underline the fraction that is equivalent to $\dfrac{3}{5}$.

$\dfrac{13}{15}$ $\dfrac{12}{20}$ $\dfrac{8}{24}$ $\dfrac{21}{25}$ $\dfrac{7}{28}$ $\dfrac{11}{34}$

2 marks

5) Complete these fractions to make each one equivalent to $\dfrac{3}{7}$.

$\dfrac{12}{⬚}$ $\dfrac{⬚}{21}$ $\dfrac{⬚}{56}$ $\dfrac{18}{⬚}$

2 marks

Fractions

6) Write each pair of fractions with the same denominator.

$\frac{1}{2}$ and $\frac{1}{3}$: ⬜/⬜ and ⬜/⬜ $\frac{2}{9}$ and $\frac{1}{6}$: ⬜/⬜ and ⬜/⬜

_____
2 marks

7) Here is a list of fractions.

$\frac{4}{5}$ $\frac{3}{10}$ $1\frac{1}{15}$ $\frac{3}{20}$ $1\frac{13}{25}$

If you're not sure what goes where, try writing the fractions over the same denominator.

Write these fractions in the correct boxes on the number line below.

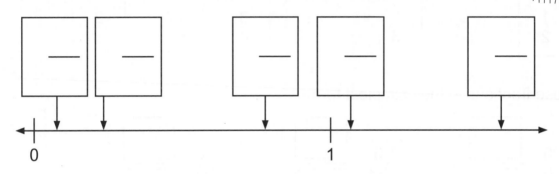

_____
1 mark

8) Convert each of these mixed numbers to improper fractions.

$1\frac{1}{5}$ .... $2\frac{3}{4}$ .... $10\frac{7}{9}$ ....

_____
2 marks

9) Convert each of these improper fractions to mixed numbers.

$\frac{11}{2}$ .... $\frac{23}{7}$ .... $\frac{65}{12}$ ....

_____
2 marks

10) Fill in the missing fractions in this sequence.

$3\frac{4}{5}$ $3\frac{2}{5}$ 3 $2\frac{⬜}{⬜}$ $2\frac{1}{5}$ $1\frac{⬜}{⬜}$ $1\frac{2}{5}$

_____
1 mark

What is the last fraction in the sequence that is **bigger than zero**?

....
_____
1 mark

A fully grown Number Adder can deal with any fraction or mixed number you throw at it. Can you?

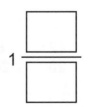

Percentages

To find 10% of something, just divide it by 10. Twice that is 20% and half is 5% — easy peasy.

1) Rafe has drawn the shape below.

What percentage of this shape is shaded?

........................%

Rafe wants 50% of the shape to be shaded.

How many more squares does he need to shade?

.... *squares*

2 marks

2) Emily is running an **800 m** race. She has run **70%** of the distance already.
How far has she run so far? Show your working in the box.

.... *m*

2 marks

3) A maths test is out of 25 marks.
The marks that Andy, Bella and Corina got on the test are shown in the table.

Student	Mark out of 25
Andy	20
Bella	15
Corina	22

You'll need to find each mark as a percentage — write each as a fraction of 25 first, then convert.

Are these statements true or false? Circle your answers.

All of the students got more than 50% in the test.   **TRUE / FALSE**

Corina got over 90% in the test.   **TRUE / FALSE**

The difference between Andy's and Bella's marks was 20%.   **TRUE / FALSE** _____

2 marks

100% of Number Adders are experts at percentages.
Are you? Tick the box to show how you got on.

Section 1 — Number and Ratio

Decimals, Fractions and Percentages

Have a go at these questions on converting between decimals, fractions and percentages.

1) Write these decimals as percentages and fractions.
   Give all fractions in their simplest form. One has been done for you.

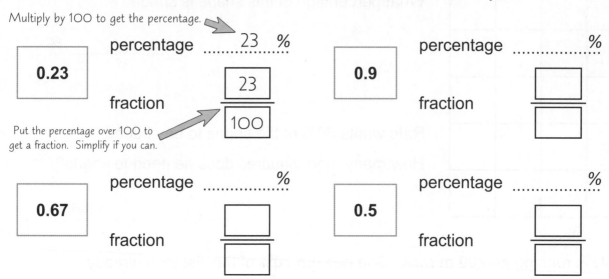

Multiply by 100 to get the percentage.

0.23 percentage .... 23 %

fraction $\dfrac{23}{100}$

Put the percentage over 100 to get a fraction. Simplify if you can.

0.9 percentage .... %

fraction

0.67 percentage .... %

fraction

0.5 percentage .... %

fraction

3 marks

2) Complete this table. Give all fractions in their simplest form.

Percentage	Fraction	Decimal
80%	....	....
....	$\dfrac{13}{50}$	....
....	....	0.45

3 marks

3) Write the values below in the correct boxes on the number line.

$\dfrac{2}{5}$ 0.15   28% $\dfrac{1}{4}$ 0.079

0 .... 0.5

1 mark

Switching between decimals, fractions and percentages is easy for a Number Adder. How did you find it?

Proportion and Ratio

Test your understanding of proportion and ratio with these questions.

1) On a school trip, there is **one** teacher for every **ten** students.
   There are **6** teachers on the trip.

   How many students are there?   .... *students*

2) Charlie and Olaf have eaten 15 sweets from a bag.
   Olaf ate twice as many sweets as Charlie.

   Try different numbers to find the ones that work.

   How many sweets did Olaf eat?   .... *sweets*

3) Four identical apples weigh **360 g**. How much would seven apples weigh?
   Show your working in the box.

   .... *g*

4) A witch is making a magic potion.
   The ingredients shown on the right
   make **one bottle** of potion.

   The witch is going to use **10 turnips**
   to make some magic potion.

   Magic Potion:

   300 ml Yucky Slime

   120 g Pixie Dust

   2 Turnips

   How many bottles of potion will she make?

   .... *bottles*

   How much yucky slime will she use?

   .... *ml*

   How much pixie dust will she use?

   .... *g*

Proportion and Ratio

5) A square has sides that are **3 cm** long.

The square is enlarged by a scale factor of **7**.

How long are the sides of the enlarged square?

.... *cm*

6) On the grid below, shape B is an enlargement of shape A.

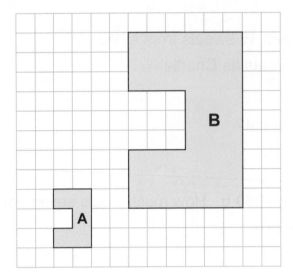

What is the scale factor of this enlargement?

....

If shape **B** was enlarged by a scale factor of **2**,
how many squares **tall** would it be?

.... *squares*

7) Wendy has a map of her town.

On the map, the school and the cinema
are **2 cm** apart, and the school and
the bakery are **3 cm** apart.

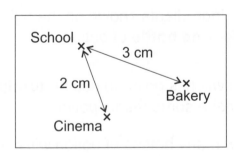

In real life, the school and the cinema
are **600 m** apart.

How far apart are the school and the bakery in real life?
Show your working in the box.

.... *m*

Proportion and Ratio

8) A farmer keeps cows and sheep.

There are **3 cows** for every **7 sheep**.

Write down the ratio of cows to sheep.

☐ : ☐

The farmer has **42** sheep. How many cows does the farmer have?

.... *cows*

_____
2 marks

9) The ratio of cars to motorbikes on a road is **8 : 5**.
There are **20** motorbikes on the road.

How many **more** cars than motorbikes are there? Show your working.

....

_____
2 marks

10) A bag contains red, green and blue counters.

For each red counter, there are two green counters and three blue counters.

The bag contains **16** green counters.

How many red counters are there?

.... *counters*

How many blue counters are there?

.... *counters*

_____
2 marks

11) Harriet's bookshelf contains fiction and non-fiction books in the ratio 3 : 2.

There are 25 books on Harriet's bookshelf.

How many books are there of each type? Show your working.

Fiction: .... *books*   Non-fiction: .... *books*

_____
2 marks

Number Adders have brains and good looks in the ratio
3 : 2. How did you find this topic? Tick the box.

Section 1 — Number and Ratio

Multiples, Factors and Primes

Two terms you'll come across in this topic are 'common multiple' and 'common factor' — they're used when the same number is a multiple or factor of two other numbers.

1) List the first 5 multiples of these numbers. One has been done for you.

   3   3, 6, 9, 12, 15 ⟵ The multiples of a number are the numbers in its times table.

   11 ....

   1 mark

2) Look at the numbers below.

   Circle all of the multiples of **4**. Underline all of the multiples of **7**.

32	34	35	38	42	46	48	49	50

   2 marks

3) Look at these digit cards.

   1   2   3   7

   Use **two** of the cards to make a two-digit number which is:

   a multiple of 8 ....   a factor of 24 ....

   a multiple of 9 ....   a factor of 46 ....

   2 marks

4) Find a common multiple of each of the following pairs of numbers.

   3 and **7** : ....   **5** and **9** : ....   **6** and **11** : ....

   2 marks

5) Alexis has sorted the numbers 20 to 30 into the table below.

   She has put one of the numbers in the wrong place.

   Put a cross through this number.

	multiple of 4	not a multiple of 4
multiple of 3	24	21, 27, 30
not a multiple of 3	20, 26, 28	22, 23, 25, 29

   1 mark

Multiples, Factors and Primes

6) Write down all the factor pairs of **60** in the box below. One has been done for you.

> 1 and 60 ← Every number has at least two factors: 1 and itself.

1 mark

7) Circle the common factors of **16** and **24** in the box below.

1	2	3	4	5
	6	7	8	9

1 mark

8) List the first **six** prime numbers.

....

1 mark

9) Circle the number below that is **not** a prime number.

37   47   57   67

1 mark

10) Write a prime number in each box to make these calculations correct.

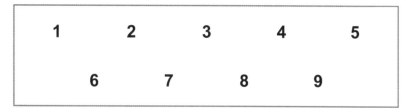

□ × □ = 35

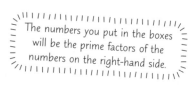
The numbers you put in the boxes will be the prime factors of the numbers on the right-hand side.

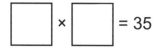

□ × □ × □ = 50

□ × □ × □ × □ = 16

2 marks

Section 1 — Number and Ratio

Multiples, Factors and Primes

11) Jamal is counting the factors of different numbers.

He finds a number that has **three** factors.

Is this number prime? Circle: **YES** or **NO**

Explain your answer below.

....

....

1 mark

12) Which prime number is a factor of **all** of the numbers in the box below?

| 56 | 42 | 350 | 49 |

....

1 mark

13) The diagrams below are called **factor trees**.

Each number is split into two factors.
These factors are written in the boxes underneath the number.
This is done until only prime numbers are left.

One of the factor trees below has been done for you. Complete the other one.

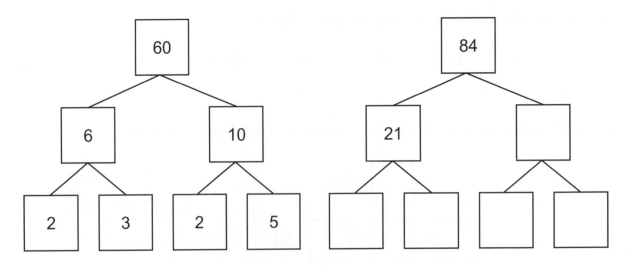

1 mark

Square and Cube Numbers

Have a go at these questions to see what you know about square and cube numbers.

1) Which number squared gives you **nine**?

.... _____
1 mark

2) What is the **sum** of four squared and five squared?

.... _____
1 mark

3) Work out the value of these square numbers.

> Use the first two answers here to work out the last answer.

6^2 ....

10^2 ....

60^2 .... _____
3 marks

4) Which two square numbers add together to make **45**?

☐ and ☐

Give two square numbers that have a difference of **99**.

☐ and ☐ _____
2 marks

5) Put all the numbers below in the correct section of the table.
One has been done for you.

3   4   5   6   10   12   25

	square number	not a square number
factor of 12	....	3 ....
factor of 50	....	....

3 is a factor of 12 but is <u>not</u> a square number.

2 marks

Section 1 — Number and Ratio

Square and Cube Numbers

6) Circle **all** of the cube numbers in the box below.

| 8 | 12 | 24 | 27 | 60 | 64 | 125 | 130 |

Which of these numbers is **also** a square number?

....

2 marks

7) Work out the value of $3^3 + 5^3$.

....

1 mark

8) Look at the numbers in the box.
Circle the number that is equal to 30^3.
Underline the number that is equal to 50^3.

| 90 | 150 | 9000 | 12 500 | 27 000 | 100 000 | 125 000 | 270 000 |

2 marks

9) Erin's age is a **square** number.
Her grandfather's age is a **cube** number.
Erin is **55** years younger than her grandfather.

How old are Erin and her grandfather?

Erin: .... *years old*   Grandfather: .... *years old*

1 mark

Number Adders love all the different kinds of numbers.
How much do you like square and cube numbers?

Adding and Subtracting

Being able to add and subtract confidently will help you conquer loads of maths topics.
Try these questions to see whether your skills are up to scratch.

1) Circle two numbers in the box that have a difference of **19**.

Underline the number that is equal to the difference between **137** and **89**.

| 15 | 27 | 32 | 48 | 50 | 69 |

_____
2 marks

2) Fill in the missing numbers in the additions below.

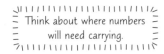

Think about where numbers will need carrying.

```
  1  9  8  3
  2  6  4  7
+    1  0  1
_____
[          ]
```

```
+     9  7  6  5
_____
  1   8  5  6  9
```

_____
2 marks

3) Adi made a drink with the following ingredients:

1250 ml apple juice   **875 ml orange juice**   **95 ml cherry juice**

How much drink did he make?

.... *ml*
_____
1 mark

4) Yona is writing a **five thousand** word story.
So far, she has written **1437** words of it.
How many more words does she have left to write?

Pick out the important numbers and decide what the question is asking you to do with them.

.... *words*
_____
1 mark

Adding and Subtracting

5) A vet weighs three rabbits. Their masses are shown below.

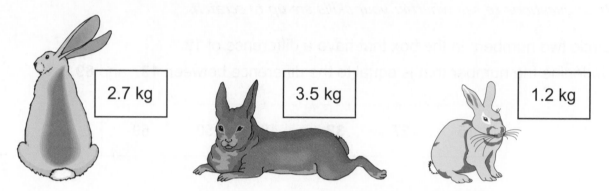

2.7 kg   3.5 kg   1.2 kg

What is the difference in mass between the heaviest and lightest rabbit?

.... kg

1 mark

6) Jodie sells cakes in the school playground.

She makes **£15.37** on Monday, and **£8.92** on Tuesday.
On Wednesday she has to spend **five pounds** on more ingredients.

How much money does she have left after Wednesday?
Show your working in the box.

£ ....

2 marks

7) Caleb is on a **40 mile** walk.

He walks **13.26 miles** before his first rest stop,
and another **9.9 miles** before his second rest stop.

How much further does he have left to walk? Show your working in the box.

.... *miles*

2 marks

All good Number Adders are Number Subtractors too!
How did you find these questions? Tick the box.

Adding and Subtracting Fractions

To add or subtract two fractions you'll need to put both over a common denominator.

1) Circle the fraction in the box that is the sum of $\frac{2}{7}$ and $\frac{3}{7}$.

$$\frac{6}{49} \qquad \frac{5}{14} \qquad \frac{6}{7} \qquad \frac{5}{7} \qquad \frac{1}{7}$$

1 mark

2) Work out the missing fractions. Give your answers in their simplest form.

$$\frac{8}{9} - \frac{7}{18} = \frac{\boxed{}}{\boxed{}} \qquad\qquad \frac{3}{4} + \frac{\boxed{}}{\boxed{}} = 1\frac{1}{4}$$

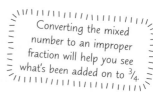

Converting the mixed number to an improper fraction will help you see what's been added on to $\frac{3}{4}$.

2 marks

3) Rahul has baked a tray of flapjack.

He gives $\frac{1}{6}$ of the tray to his neighbour, and then takes $\frac{3}{5}$ of the tray into school.

What fraction of the tray of flapjack is left? Show your working out in the box.

2 marks

4) Rita does the following subtraction: $\quad 4\frac{2}{3} - 1\frac{14}{15} = 3\frac{4}{15}$

Is she correct? Circle: **YES / NO**.

Explain how you know.

....

....

1 mark

A coiled Number Adder will spring into action to do questions on fractions... But how about you?

Section 2 — Calculations

Multiplying and Dividing

Have a go at the questions on the next few pages to see how well you can multiply and divide.

1) Tick the boxes next to all the **correct** calculations.

    ☐ 8 × 7 = 54   ☐ 84 ÷ 12 = 7

    ☐ 11 × 11 = 121   ☐ 72 ÷ 9 = 6

    ☐ 6 × 9 = 58   ☐ 108 ÷ 9 = 9

    1 mark

2) Jason buys **three** poetry books for **£24**. They each have the same price.

    What is the price of **one** book?

    £ ....

    How much would he pay for **twelve** books at this price?

    £ ....

    2 marks

3) Nine friends win an equal share of **£558** in a competition.
    How much does each person win?

    £ ....

    1 mark

4) A comedian performs a show
    every night for **27** nights.

    Each night, **253** people
    come to see the show.

    How many people see
    the show in total?
    Show your working.

    .... *people*

    2 marks

Multiplying and Dividing

5) Aaron is trying to write a calculation that gives the answer **39**.

He starts by writing: | **5 + 8 × 3** |

What is the answer to Aaron's calculation?

....

Add brackets to the calculation below so that it gives the answer 39.

5 + 8 × 3

_____
2 marks

6) In the box, write a calculation using the digits 3, 7 and 9 to give the answer **42**.
Use each digit **once**.

You can use brackets and any of
the four operations (+, −, × and ÷).

_____
1 mark

7) **85** children enter a maths contest.
They need to be split into teams, with a maximum of **6** children on each team.
What is the smallest possible number of teams needed?

.... *teams*

_____
1 mark

8) Beth buys a large bag of **250** sugar-coated almonds.
She splits them into smaller gift bags, with **7** almonds in each bag.

How many of these smaller gift bags can she fill?

.... *bags*

How many almonds will be left over?

.... *almonds*

_____
2 marks

Section 2 — Calculations

Multiplying and Dividing

9) Draw lines between the boxes to complete the calculations.
One has been done for you.

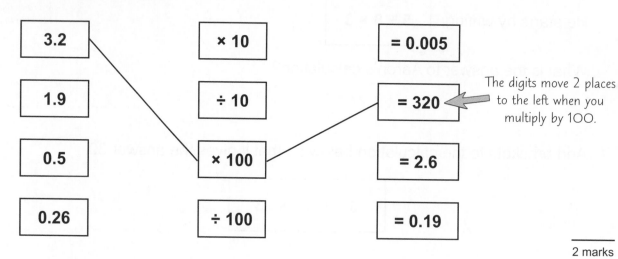

The digits move 2 places to the left when you multiply by 100.

2 marks

10) Write the answer to each division in the boxes.

365 ÷ 10 = ☐   94 ÷ 100 = ☐   798 ÷ 1000 = ☐

2 marks

11) Circle the number in each box that makes the calculation correct.

| 29 |
| 290 | ÷ 1000 = 0.29 |
| 2900 |

| 1.6 |
| 10.6 | × 100 = 106 |
| 1.06 |

1 mark

12) Write the missing numbers in the boxes.

☐ × 1000 = 830   267 ÷ ☐ = 2.67

100 × ☐ × 0.382 = 3820   68 ÷ ☐ = 0.1

2 marks

13) What number should **594** be divided by to make **100**?

....

1 mark

Multiplying and Dividing

14) Circle the calculation that gives a **different** answer to the others.

| 4 × 6 × 20 | 10 × 6 × 8 | 2 × 30 × 6 | 3 × 4 × 40 |

_____
1 mark

15) Tick the boxes next to all the divisions that have a remainder of **3**.

☐ 58 ÷ 9   ☐ 45 ÷ 6   ☐ 98 ÷ 5   ☐ 64 ÷ 7

_____
1 mark

16) A brick has a height of **1.7 cm**. How high is a tower that is **eight** bricks tall?

.... cm

_____
1 mark

17) Keiko has **14** jugs of squash.

Each jug contains **1285 ml** of squash.

How much squash does Keiko have? Show your working out in the box.

.... ml

_____
2 marks

18) There are **962** pupils in a school.

The pupils are split into **26** classes of equal size.

How many pupils are there in each class? Show your working out in the box.

Use long division here.

....

_____
2 marks

Number Adders love to divide, but did these questions make you want to hide? Tick the box to say how you feel.

Multiplying and Dividing Fractions

Now it's time to try some questions on multiplying and dividing with fractions.

1) Circle the two fractions in the box that multiply to give $\frac{8}{15}$.

$\frac{2}{3}$	$\frac{4}{3}$	$\frac{4}{5}$	$\frac{2}{15}$	$\frac{4}{15}$

1 mark

2) Nine friends each eat $\frac{2}{3}$ of a pizza.

How many pizzas do they eat in total?

.... *pizzas*

1 mark

3) Five people share $\frac{3}{5}$ of a pot of stew equally between them.

Benji thinks they have $\frac{1}{3}$ of the pot of stew each.

Is he correct? Circle: **YES / NO**.

Explain how you know.

....

....

1 mark

4) Fill in the boxes with the missing numbers.

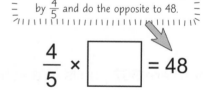

Think about how you would multiply by $\frac{4}{5}$ and do the opposite to 48.

$\frac{7}{9} \times 18 = \boxed{}$

$\frac{1}{6} \times \frac{\boxed{}}{\boxed{}} = \frac{1}{24}$

$\frac{4}{5} \times \boxed{} = 48$

3 marks

5) Fill in the boxes. Give your answers in their simplest form.

$\frac{5}{6} \div 5 = \frac{\boxed{}}{\boxed{}}$

$\frac{7}{8} \div 3 = \frac{\boxed{}}{\boxed{}}$

$\frac{2}{9} \div 4 = \frac{\boxed{}}{\boxed{}}$

3 marks

Number Adders can get their head (and body) around fractions questions with no fuss. How about you?

Checking and Estimating

You can check the answers to calculations by estimating or doing inverse calculations.

1) Daisy pays for a **67p** bag of crisps with a **£1** coin. She gets **33p** change.
   Write an addition that she can use to check she has got the right change.

   $\boxed{\qquad}\,p$ + $\boxed{\qquad}\,p$ = $\boxed{\qquad}\,p$

   _____
   1 mark

2) Fill in the boxes with **+**, **−**, **×** or **÷** to make each sentence correct.

   893 + 42 = 935, so 935 $\boxed{\qquad}$ 42 = 893

   67 × 84 = 5628, so 5628 $\boxed{\qquad}$ 67 = 84

   999 − 367 = 632, so 999 $\boxed{\qquad}$ 632 = 367

   _____
   3 marks

3) Ben wants to check that the division **192 ÷ 16 = 12** is correct.
   Which calculation below could he **not** use to check this?
   Circle your answer.

   | 12 × 16 = 192 | | 12 ÷ 192 = 16 | | 192 ÷ 12 = 16 |

   _____
   1 mark

4) The perimeter of a square is found using the formula: **Perimeter = 4 × Side Length**
   Which of these is the correct inverse calculation? Tick the box.

   $\square$ Side Length = 4 × Perimeter

   $\square$ Side Length = Perimeter ÷ 4

   $\square$ Side Length × Perimeter = 4

   $\square$ Side Length ÷ 4 = Perimeter

   _____
   1 mark

Checking and Estimating

5) Fill in the missing numbers to give a different calculation
   that uses the same numbers as the one on the left.

805 + 234 = 1039 ⟶ ☐ – ☐ = ☐

2304 ÷ 24 = 96 ⟶ ☐ × ☐ = ☐

984 ÷ 82 = 12 ⟶ ☐ ÷ ☐ = ☐

_____
3 marks

6) Huw needs to buy one of each of the following items:

Toy dinosaur:	£5.99
Paperclips:	£1.05
Pencil case:	£2.95

Estimate how much this will cost in total.

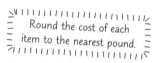
Round the cost of each
item to the nearest pound.

£............................

_____
1 mark

7) By rounding to the nearest whole number, estimate the answer to **7.3 × 11.8**.
   Fill in the boxes with your calculation.

☐ × ☐ = ☐

_____
1 mark

8) Becca calculates that **283 × 62 = 1756**.
   Use **estimation** to show that she has made a mistake.

....

....

_____
1 mark

Checking and Estimating

9) Look at the calculation in the box: | **12 341 ÷ 43 = 287**

Use this to find the answers to the calculations below. One has been done for you.

430 is 10 times
bigger than 43.

So the answer
will be 10 times
smaller than 287.

12 341 ÷ 430 = ...28.7........................

123.41 ÷ 43 = ...

1 234 100 ÷ 43 = ...

12 341 ÷ 4.3 = ...

_____
2 marks

10) By rounding to the nearest 10, estimate the answer to **203.1 ÷ 20**.

$$\boxed{} \div 20 = \boxed{}$$

Is this estimate larger or smaller than the real answer?

Circle: **Larger / Smaller**.

_____
2 marks

11) Circle the number that gives the best estimate to $\frac{20}{3} + \frac{17}{4}$.

| 9 | 10 | 11 | 12 | 13 | 14 |

_____
1 mark

12) By rounding each fraction to the nearest whole number, estimate the answer to:

$$3\frac{2}{3} \times 2\frac{1}{4} - 4\frac{3}{5}$$

....

_____
1 mark

*Now's the time to check how you got on with these
questions. How do you compare to a Number Adder?*

Wordy Problems

The trick with wordy problems is picking out the important numbers and working out what the question is asking you to do with them. Have a go at these questions.

1) Three friends are getting the bus together.

They want to go into town, then come back again. The ticket options are:

One-way:	£2.20 per person
Return:	£4.00 per person
Group return:	£13.00 for up to 4 people

Read the question carefully — the three friends make two journeys each.

Which ticket option has the **lowest** total cost? Tick the box.

☐ Two one-way tickets each   ☐ A return ticket each

☐ One group return ticket

What is the total cost of the **most expensive** option for the three friends?

£ ....   _____

2 marks

2) Jessie is saving money to pay for a holiday.
The total cost of the holiday is **£800**.
Jessie has already saved up **one quarter** of the total cost.

How much more does she need to save up?

£ ....   _____

1 mark

Jessie earns **£150** each week and saves **one third** of this for the holiday.

How many more weeks will it take to save up the rest of the cost of the holiday?
Show your working out in the box.

      .... *weeks*

2 marks

Wordy Problems

3) Anya is making stock by adding stock cubes to boiling water.

   To dissolve one stock cube, she needs 450 ml of boiling water.

   How much water will she need for **three** stock cubes?

   .... ml

   What is the **smallest whole number** of stock cubes
   she will need to make **at least 2000 ml** of stock?

   ⌐⌐⌐⌐⌐⌐⌐⌐⌐⌐⌐⌐⌐⌐⌐⌐⌐
   'At least 2000 ml' means
   '2000 ml or more'.
   ⌐⌐⌐⌐⌐⌐⌐⌐⌐⌐⌐⌐⌐⌐⌐⌐⌐

   .... cubes   _____
   2 marks

4) Each robot in a chocolate factory can wrap **20** chocolate bars every minute.

   Which of these would wrap the **most** chocolate bars? Tick the box.

   ☐ 4 robots in 10 mins

   ☐ 3 robots in 25 mins

   ☐ 1 robot in 1 hour

   How many chocolate bars will be wrapped in this case?

   .... chocolate bars   _____
   2 marks

5) Sofie and Carsten have the same birthday.

   On their next birthday, Sofie will be one and a half times as old as Carsten.

   If Carsten is **ten** years old on that day, how many years **older** will Sofie be?

   .... years

   What will be the **sum** of their ages on their birthday **five years later**?

   .... years   _____
   2 marks

Section 3 — Problem Solving and Algebra

Wordy Problems

6) Five silver coins are worth the same as three gold coins.

Two gold coins are worth the same as eleven bronze coins.

How many **bronze** coins are worth the same as **ten silver coins**?
Show your working out in the box.

.... bronze coins

2 marks

7) Graeme lives in Anniesland, and is planning a trip to Balloch.

He wants to spend at least **4 hours** in Balloch,
but he needs to be back in Anniesland by **4 pm**.

Graeme looks up the train timetable for the day.
The available trains are shown below.

Depart Anniesland	Arrive Balloch
0855	0930
0945	1020
1035	1110

Depart Balloch	Arrive Anniesland
1355	1430
1445	1520
1535	1610

What is the latest train from Anniesland he can take in the morning?
Circle your answer.

0855	0945	1035

In total, how many minutes will he spend on a train throughout the day?

.... minutes

2 marks

*Number Adders have no problem when it comes to
problem solving. How about you? Tick the box.*

Patterns and Sequences

Practise spotting the rules for patterns and sequences with these questions.

1) Taz writes a sequence of numbers with the following rule:

> **"Add fifteen to get the next number in the sequence."**

Fill in the missing numbers in Taz's sequence.

[ ]   **31**   **46**   **61**   [ ]

1 mark

2) Write down the rule to find the next term in this number sequence.

48   **24**   **12**   **6**   **3**   ...

Think of different ways of getting from one number to the next, and see which works for all the numbers.

....

1 mark

3) Circle the number in each box that fits the sequence.

19   26 | **29** | 40   47 | **54** |
                | **31** | | **56** |
                | **33** | | **58** |

1 mark

) Look at this sequence of numbers:

5   **10**   **15**   **25**   **40**   **65**

What is the rule for the sequence? Tick the box.

[ ] Multiply by 2

[ ] Add 5

[ ] Add up the previous two numbers

1 mark

Patterns and Sequences

5) Abbie writes a sequence of numbers on white and grey tiles, as shown:

| 3 | 6 | 9 | 12 | 15 |

What number would go on the next **white** tile?

....

Abbie thinks that the number 30 would go on a **white** tile.

Is she correct? Circle: **YES / NO**.

Explain how you know.

....

....

6) Here is a sequence of patterns made from circles.

Draw the next pattern in the sequence in the box below.

Look at how the number of dots is connected to the position of the pattern in the sequence — e.g. Pattern 1 = 4 dots, Pattern 2 = 8 dots.

How many circles will be in the **tenth** pattern in the sequence?   ....

Patterns and Sequences

7) Match each sequence to its rule. One has been done for you.

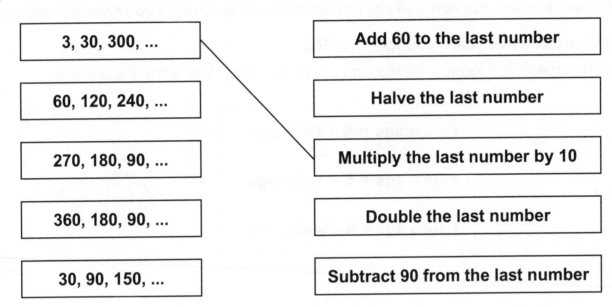

3, 30, 300, ...	Add 60 to the last number
60, 120, 240, ...	Halve the last number
270, 180, 90, ...	Multiply the last number by 10
360, 180, 90, ...	Double the last number
30, 90, 150, ...	Subtract 90 from the last number

2 marks

8) Fill in the missing number in the sequence below.

5   15   45   135   [ ]

1 mark

Write down the rule for the sequence.

....

1 mark

9) For each sequence below, tick the box if the number **35** is part of the sequence.

[ ] 7, 14, 21, ...

[ ] 13, 19, 25, ...

[ ] 45, 42, 39, ...

[ ] 280, 140, 70, ...

2 marks

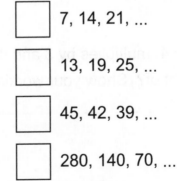

Sssequences are sssimple for Number Adders.
How well can you ssspot patterns in numbers?

Section 3 — Problem Solving and Algebra

Formulas

Formulas are calculations written with words or letters that show you how to work out one quantity from another. See how well you can use formulas by having a go at these questions.

1) Peta is exactly **five years younger** than Rei.

   Which of these is a formula for working out Peta's age? Underline the answer.

   > **Peta's age = 5 × Rei's age**
   >
   > **Peta's age = 5 + Rei's age**
   >
   > **Peta's age = Rei's age − 5**

   Think about what you'd do to Rei's age to get to Peta's age.

   1 mark

2) May uses this formula to work out the amount of eggs in a muffin recipe:

   Number of eggs = Number of muffins ÷ 12

   How many eggs does May need to make **48** muffins?

   .... *eggs*

   1 mark

   The recipe uses half as much sugar as flour.
   Write a formula in words for working out the
   amount of flour from the amount of sugar.

   Look at how the other formulas on the page are written.

   ....

   1 mark

3) Mike thinks of a number, subtracts 4, multiplies by 3 and then adds 2 to get **23**.
   What was the number Mike thought of? Show your working out in the box.

   ....

   2 marks

Formulas

4) The area of a triangle can be found using the following formula:

$$\textbf{Area of a triangle} = \frac{1}{2} \times \textbf{Base} \times \textbf{Height}$$

What is the area of the triangle below?

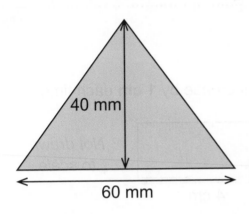

40 mm

60 mm

...................................mm^2

1 mark

5) Steve is making a model of his garden. The model has bees and flowers.
    For every bee in the model, Steve makes **eight** flowers.

 = number of bees   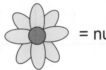 = number of flowers

Which of these formulas is **not** correct? Put a cross in the box.

☐   🐝 = 🌼 ÷ 8

☐   🐝 = 8 × 🌼

☐   🌼 = 8 × 🐝

1 mark

If the model contains **56** flowers, how many bees are there?

.... *bees*

1 mark

Section 3 — Problem Solving and Algebra

Formulas

6) The cost C, in £, of hiring a hoverboard for H hours is: **C = (5 × H) + 6**

Find the cost of hiring the hoverboard for **3** hours.

£ ....

1 mark

7) Taylor makes a sequence of rectangles.

Each rectangle has a height of **2 cm**, but the widths increase by **1 cm** each time:

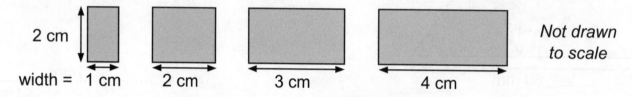

2 cm

Not drawn to scale

width =   1 cm   2 cm   3 cm   4 cm

Fill in the table to show the perimeter of the next rectangle in the sequence.

Width in cm (w)	1	2	3	4	5
Perimeter in cm (p)	6	8	10	12	

1 mark

Fill in the boxes to give a formula that links the perimeter (**p**) with the width (**w**).

p = (☐ × **w**) + ☐

1 mark

8) There are **S** sheep and **C** chickens in a field.

The number of animal legs (L) in the field can be found using the formula:

$$L = (4 × S) + (2 × C)$$

If there are **100** animal legs in a field, and **20** sheep,
how many chickens are there? Show your working in the box.

.... *chickens*

2 marks

Formulas

9) Ellen spells her name with letter tiles in a game.

Each letter has a different value,
and each value is a multiple of 5.

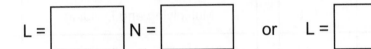

The letter 'E' has a value of **5**.
The total value of Ellen's name is **60**.

Write down **two** possible pairs of values for the letters 'L' and 'N' in these boxes.

L = ☐ N = ☐   or   L = ☐ N = ☐

_____
2 marks

10) Ash is making bracelets with two types of bead on a wire.

The wire is free, but the beads have a cost per bead.

Ash makes two different bracelets:

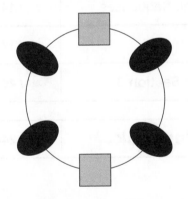

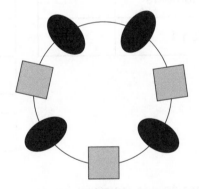

Total cost = 74p   Total cost = 89p

> Look at what's different between the two bracelets and work out the effect this has on the cost.

Calculate the cost of each bead. Show your working out in the box.

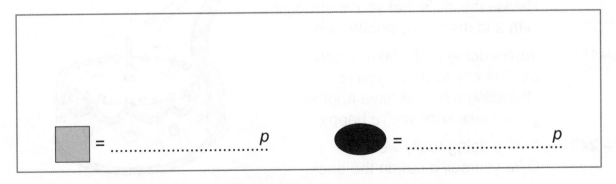

☐ = ... p   ⬤ = ... p

_____
2 marks

Number Adders know the magic formula for getting
better at maths — practice! How did you get on?

Section 3 — Problem Solving and Algebra

Scoresheet

Fill in your scores below as you work through the book.
Once you get to the end of each section, find your total marks to see how you're getting on.

Section 1	Score
Place Value and Roman Numerals	/ 10
Ordering Numbers and Rounding	/ 22
Decimals	/ 16
Fractions	/ 18
Percentages	/ 6
Decimals, Fractions and Percentages	/ 7
Proportion and Ratio	/ 20
Multiples, Factors and Primes	/ 17
Square and Cube Numbers	/ 15
Total for Section 1	**/ 131**

Section 2	Score
Adding and Subtracting	/ 11
Adding and Subtracting Fractions	/ 6
Multiplying and Dividing	/ 27
Multiplying and Dividing Fractions	/ 9
Checking and Estimating	/ 18
Total for Section 2	**/ 71**

Section 3	Score
Wordy Problems	/ 15
Patterns and Sequences	/ 14
Formulas	/ 17
Total for Section 3	**/ 46**

Total for Book	**/ 248**

Look at your total score to see how you're doing and where you need more practice:

0 – 139 — Don't worry if you got lots wrong. Revise the skills that you're struggling with and then have another go.

140 – 199 — You're doing well. Take a look back at any sections you're struggling with and have another go to make sure you're happy.

200 – 248 — You're doing really well. Give yourself a pat on the back.